The Bounty Bible

The Bounty Bible

Ian Barclay

Illustrated by
Lynette Hardwick

BISHOPSGATE PRESS LTD

© Ian Barclay 1993
British Library Cataloguing in Publication Data
Barclay, Ian
 The Bounty Bible.
    1. Great Britain. Royal Navy. Sailing Vessels :
    Bounty (Ship). Mutiny
    I. Title
    359.1334

    ISBN 1 - 85219 - 052 - 3
    Copyright Material:

    Short quotation (p 190) from FRAGILE
    PARADISE: The Discovery of Fletcher Christian
    Bounty Mutineer by Glynn Christian (Hamish
    Hamilton, 1982) copyright Glyn Christian,
    1982. Reproduced by permission of Hamish
    Hamilton Ltd.

All enquiries and requests relevant to this title
should be sent to the publishers,

Bishopsgate Press Ltd.,
Bartholomew House,
15, Tonbridge Road,
Hildenborough, Kent TN11 9BH

Printed by Whitstable Litho Printers Ltd.,
Whitstable, Kent.

The Bounty Bible

Captain Mayhew Folger, of the American whaling ship *Topaz,* stared with astonishment at the circle of happy women and children who had gathered for family prayers outside John Adams' house on Pitcairn Island. He made a note of the date; it was the 6th February 1808. He knew that when he returned to Boston, in America, he would have to report that he had discovered what had happened to HMS *Bounty*. He also knew he would have to describe the nearly perfect community he had found on Pitcairn.

John Adams had the Bounty's Bible in his hands.
He had just read from it, as he always did during
the island's daily worship time. He said a final
prayer and then the Tahitian women and children
left for their work in the fields, just as they would
have done if they had been back at home in Tahiti.

It was twenty-three years since the *Bounty* had left England. John Adams was the only English sailor left. The rest of the crew had died or been killed, and a few had escaped in an open boat. This is their story. An adventure of the high seas, and also a story of how a ship's Bible turned an island of unhappy people into one of the happiest places on earth.

Fletcher Christian was born on the 25th September 1764 in a large house in the foothills of the Lake District. His home was a medieval manor, half castle and half farm. He had an exciting childhood full of adventure with streams to fish, hills to climb and woods and valleys to explore on his piebald pony. While he was still a boy there were two tragedies in his family, his father died when he was four years old and his mother's side of the family became bankrupt when he was sixteen. So, in 1780 with a very small amount of money, she took Fletcher and her other two young children, to Douglas in the Isle of Man. Fletcher Christian could no longer expect the easy life of a well-to-do family, he would have to find a job and so it was that he met William Bligh in Douglas.

Bligh was a Cornishman, born at Plymouth on 9th September 1754. He was seven years old when his name first appeared in Naval records. They refer to him becoming the Captain's servant on HMS *Montrose*. This was so that when he grew up he could be promoted quickly. No one could become a Lieutenant until he had served at sea for six years.

He was twenty when appointed midshipman on HMS *Crescent* but he signed on as an ordinary seaman two years later to serve on HMS *Ranger*. She was based at Douglas and her task was to hunt and arrest smugglers in the Irish Sea.

In the eighteenth century, England owned a lot of land in the West Indies. Slaves were taken there from Africa to work in the sugar plantations. Most of the food for the slaves had to be taken to the West Indies all the way from England. This expensive way of feeding them meant that the price of a bag of sugar was very high in England.

The Government tried to find something that would grow quickly and easily in the West Indies. They heard that on the other side of the world, on a Pacific island called Tahiti, was a tree that produced fruit with white pulp like new bread. They were told that a good sized tree could yield a constant crop of Bread-fruit, which could be eaten raw or cooked. The weather in the West Indies was similar to that in the Pacific so it seemed that the cultivation of Bread-fruit trees might be a way of providing cheap food for slaves.

The Government decided to pay for an expedition to sail to Tahiti, collect a cargo of young Bread-fruit trees and take them to Jamaica for planting. This would perhaps end the tiresome and expensive business of taking food from England.

When the Naval Board bought the *Bethia*, a coastal trader built in Hull, she was two and a half years old and lying at anchor in the Thames at Wapping Old Steps. The price paid for her was £1,895.12s.8d. On the 6th June 1787 she was towed to Deptford Naval Yard and renamed *Bounty*.

In those days, the sailor's worst enemy was shipworm, a voracious little beast that could eat up the wooden hull of a ship in no time at all. Most ships were given a second layer of timber consisting of planks $1\frac{1}{4}$ inches thick which could be replaced as they only were eaten by the shipworm. This worked very well for traders in coastal waters but was totally inadequate for a ship about to sail around the world and which would have to wait until returning home for repair. This was the *Bounty's* predicament, so she was sheathed in copper and all her fittings were replaced by those made of good, long lasting copper and brass.

Her mast was shortened to make her less top heavy, so that without too much difficulty, she would be safe in the worst storms at sea.

Finally, two platforms were put into the hold of this little snub-nosed vessel to take the 629 pots, which would eventually contain young Breadfruit trees to be taken from Tahiti to Jamaica.

The *Bounty* was 91 feet long and her crew consisted of 45 men. They were a remarkably young crew; most of them were under the age of thirty. Twenty-three year old Fletcher Christian was the Master's Mate and Lieutenant William Bligh was the oldest of the crew at 33. It was just as well that Bligh was the oldest because he was the Captain.

Life on board ship in the 18th century was not easy. The officers were issued with a uniform but the rest of the crew wore their ordinary clothes. They were, however, given a coat made of sail cloth to wear in very 'bad weather which was tarred to make it waterproof. This black and cumbersome garment made people call sailors 'tarpaulins' at first but by the time the *Bounty* sailed, the name was changed to 'Jack Tars'.

The *Bounty* began her expedition on the 23rd December 1787. But only three days out in the Atlantic, huge long swelling waves called 'rollers' smashed over the tiny ship causing her stern windows to collapse and allowing icy water to sweep through the whole vessel.

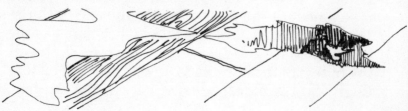

The wet and frightened sailors did not even have
the comfort of hot food because the stove would
not light. Rations of grog, which is a thick Naval
rum, was added to their beer and they had to fill
their empty stomachs on ship's biscuit.

They sailed first to the Canary Islands where they put into a port for some repairs and to restock with fresh food and 863½ gallons of wine. The *Bounty* then headed across the Atlantic towards Brazil intending to sail around Cape Horn into the Pacific Ocean.

For nearly a whole month they battled with gales off Tierra del Fuego while trying to round Cape Horn. They hardly ever had an Easterly wind to help them and they endured the most violent storms that anyone could remember. Finally, to the great relief of everyone on board, they changed direction on the 22nd April 1788, turning East and so approaching the Pacific Ocean via the tip of Africa.

Sheep, pigs and chickens had been swept from the deck of the *Bounty* when she had tried to get around Cape Horn. No fresh meat was left. The crew were cold and wet, several were injured and even more unwell. For over two months they had survived on meagre rations, such as ship's biscuit, which was dull, dry and often full of weevils. To try and improve their health Captain Bligh insisted that the crew had hot wheat and sugar with a pint of sweet malt drink for breakfast and he ordered fine rum, pickled cabbage, mustard and vinegar to be served at other meals.

CANADA

ATLANTIC OCEAN

USA

23rd Dec. 1787

UK

LONDON

EUROPE

CANARY ISLANDS

TROPIC OF CANCER

WEST INDIES

AFRICA

EQUATOR

BRAZIL
SOUTH AMERICA

ATLANTIC OCEAN

TROPIC OF CAPRICORN

CAPE TOWN
FALSE BAY

1st July 1788

CAPE OF
GOOD HOPE

TRISTAN
DA CUNHA

TIERRA DEL FUEGO

CAPE HORN

22nd April 1788

ANTARCTIC CIRCLE

17

Turning East into a following wind and better weather as they headed for Africa did not immediately solve all their problems. The crew were still sickly and it was nearly impossible to get the cooking stove to work below decks. All it produced was a heavy black smoke which filled every nook and cranny of the ship.

They tried to find the tiny island of Tristan Da Cunha as they approached Africa but failed to sight it. Eventually they dropped anchor in False Bay near Cape Town where they spent 30 days repairing the ship once more. All the stores had to be checked and made shipshape.

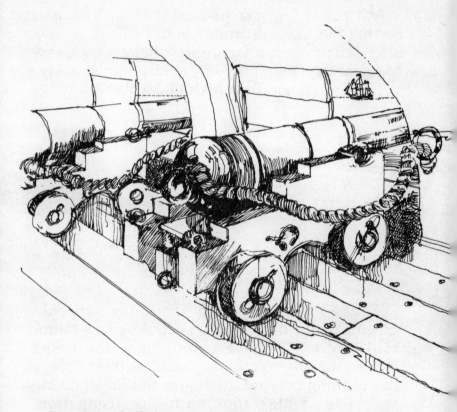

In spite of all the traumatic experiences of their perilous voyage, not one man had been lost. On 1st July 1788, with a thirteen gun salute, they set sail once more for the island of Tahiti.

After ten months at sea, the *Bounty* reached the island of Melitia just sixty miles from her destination. On 25th October, at 6 o'clock in the evening, how excited the crew must have been as they caught their first glimpse of Tahiti, lit by the last moments of the sun as it sank below the horizon.

At 4 o'clock the next morning the *Bounty* hove to so that her exact position could be fixed on the ship's charts at sunrise. Tahiti's Point Venus and Matavai Bay were only ten nautical miles away, and the wind was now little more than a breeze.

As the sun rose behind Tahiti, the dark ink-green smudge of shadows, skirted by lava-crumpled land gradually came into view. The sailors had seen many wonderful sights on their voyage but nothing prepared them for the breathtaking spectacle of high rock pinnacles rising from valleys of the brightest emerald green. As the early morning mists cleared they could see high waterfalls which appeared to merge with the wisps of smoke climbing from the early morning fires.

At 9 o'clock the *Bounty* was drifting through a gap in the reef into the lagoon of Matavai Bay. Not far away, the beach curved for about a mile, its fine black volcanic sand seeming to highlight the lush green of the island. A large flotilla of canoes had put out from the shore and soon the *Bounty* was so full of welcoming Tahitians that William Bligh could not spot his own crew. After the hardship of the past months, the sailors were dazzled by the sundrenched welcome from the people of a Pacific island.

The island that lay just across the lagoon from the *Bounty* must have looked like paradise to the sailors. Food grew abundantly and in great variety needing little or no attention. There was no cannibalism, poverty or squalor and very little disease. The people were a tall, noble race dressed in yards of brilliant white cloth. They had magnificent teeth, bathed twice a day and rubbed sweet smelling oils into their skin.

By contrast, the sailors must have looked and
felt ugly and unhealthy. They did not wash much
during a voyage, especially when the sea was cold.
The lack of fresh food and vitamins affected their
teeth and gave them bad breath, gums, skin and
hair. Rinsing their clothes in sea water would not
have got rid of the sweat and grime from months
at sea.

Tahiti had no single king but instead each district had a chief. Everything touched by a chief's feet would immediately become his property and so, for everyday business, he was carried around shoulder high by his subjects. When you met him he would expect you to bare yourself to the waist as a sign of respect. Even high collared and buttoned English officers would have to do that.

There were three different levels of society in Tahiti. The top one was really a royal family and the chiefs always belonged to this. They were tall and proud. They were also fat and pale because they would often retire for days into special thatched huts out of the sun to gorge themselves on rich food. The important landowners and minor chiefs were the next level. They could be spotted by their dress. The labouring class who were very dark skinned made up the bottom stratum of society. Each class kept to itself and would never even think of trying to be like another.

The *Bounty* carried many things to trade with the Tahitians in exchange for Bread-fruit, including 3,000 chisels, 600 knives, 150 axes, 150 mirrors, 8cwt of copper nails and well over ½cwt of glass beads. These had been purchased just before the *Bounty* sailed for the sum of £125.6s.4d. None of these items could be found on a Pacific island and so they were all highly prized by the Tahitian people.

When the *Bounty* arrived at Tahiti the crew were surprised to see that most of the people had covered their skins with permanent coloured designs called tattoos. Fletcher Christian and the crew were among the first Europeans to have these ink patterns dyed into their skin. They discovered that it was a long and painful process.

When Captain Bligh gave a description of Fletcher Christian, he said that he had been "tatowed", this was because our word *tattoo* comes from the Tahitian word *ta'tau*.

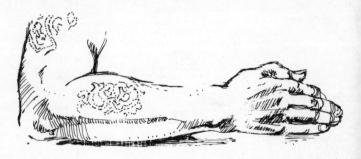

When people go to the Pacific today and see tattooed Polynesians, they think that tattooing has spread there from Europe. Of course this is not so; it all started in the Pacific and from there has come to the rest of the world.

Life was much easier in Tahiti than in Europe. Children were free to play where they chose and were never in much danger.

Teenagers devoted themselves to energetic sports, dancing and making music with very few rules and restrictions. Any work that had to be done was undertaken by the dark-skinned Manahune, who were the women of the labouring class.

The men were responsible for the cooking and early in the morning would prepare the earth ovens. After lighting the fire, food was placed on very hot stones and covered first with banana leaves and then mounds of earth which were left in place until the cooking was complete. Everybody would gather for the main meal of the day. The men and women ate separately and if a woman touched food prepared for a man it had to be thrown away. Even if she touched one of his eating implements, these were either replaced or prayed over to restore them for man's use.

Sometimes during the year the women would spend days pounding the bark of the mulberry tree to make a cloth called 'tapa'.

The high point of the year was a festival of singing and dancing called 'heiva' when everyone would dance in perfect unison.

William Bligh and his men stayed in Tahiti for six months. It is sometimes said that this was because the season for collecting Bread-fruit saplings was over when they arrived. However, there are many different kinds of Bread-fruit and one or another is in flower for most of the year. In addition, Bread-fruit do not produce seeds, but, like bananas, shoots that spring up from the roots to become new trees. So, there is no special time to look for the young trees and there must have been another explanation for the *Bounty*'s long stay.

Soon after their arrival David Nelson, the ship's botanist and his assistant William Brown, gave orders for the collection to begin. The work started on the 7th November when 110 saplings were collected and by one week later they had 774. It only took another month to complete the repairs on the *Bounty* and to make certain that the saplings had really taken root in their pots in the ship's hold.

It is not difficult to imagine the real reason for the *Bounty*'s long sojourn in Tahiti and her delay over setting sail for the Atlantic Ocean and then into the Caribbean Sea. November to April is the hurricane season and no small ship would want to venture out to sea with the possibility of being hit by a violent Pacific storm. Added to this was the fact that the men simply enjoyed themselves in the sunny earthly paradise. People did not take regular holidays in those days and the crew of the *Bounty* with their Captain, enjoyed the sun and relaxing while they could.

The *Bounty* swayed at anchor in the pleasant summer breeze of the sheltered bay. In the southern part of the world the seasons are reversed and they have their summer during our winter. Most of the sailors spent their time ashore enjoying themselves while Captain Bligh stayed on board and entertained the important chiefs and other members of the royal family who came on board the ship. Occasionally a little work had to be done when the Captain ordered more tubs to be made for the Bread-fruit saplings or parts of the ship to be cleaned and repaired.

In January three men deserted one night, stealing the ship's largest rowing-boat and eight muskets to offer as payment for any islander who would hide them. The launch was eventually found abandoned in Matavai Bay where the runaway sailors had exchanged it for a local sail-canoe and headed for Tetiaroa which is an atoll thirty miles to the north of Tahiti. Tetiaroa is only a tiny crescent of coral with a few trees and little vegetation. It is not big enough to be called an island.

Before the fugitives were caught William Bligh had another very serious problem on his hands. A new set of sails that would be needed for the return voyage were found to be rotten. The master, John Fryer and the boatswain William Cole, were responsible for keeping the unused sails in perfect order, but the Captain and his crew had relaxed a little too much, forgetting that they had a job to do.

By the beginning of March 1789 William Bligh was preparing his ship to take the Bread-fruit saplings to Jamaica. He let the ship's cats loose in his all out attempt to rid the *Bounty* of cockroaches and other insects that had multiplied vigorously while they had been riding at anchor off Tahiti. A chicken house at the stern of the ship was converted into a store for the extra containers of Bread-fruit saplings which now numbered well over a thousand.

Preparations then ceased for two weeks because the island was hit with very heavy tropical rainstorms. But by the 25th March the ship's cats were taken ashore and a live cargo of 25 pigs and 17 goats were stowed to provide fresh meat on the next part of their voyage. William Bligh told his sailors that they could take home as many souvenirs as they wished to, provided they could pack them all into the wooden chest that each sailor used for his personal belongings.

Finally, on the 4th April 1789, the wind was right for the *Bounty's* departure. Captain Bligh sent "goodbye" presents to the senior chief, Teina. These included the muskets and pistols he wanted and the ship's two dogs Venus and Bacchus, Bligh then wrote in his log, "at 5 o'clock we bade farewell to Tahiti where for twenty-three weeks we were treated with the greatest kindness and fed with the best meat and the finest fruit in the world."

Once back at sea, William Bligh had to make sure his officers and men still knew how to sail the *Bounty* safely. They would soon need the skill to sail through some difficult and dangerous stretches of water so he took advantage of the good weather in the Pacific Ocean to let the crew practice putting the sails up and taking them down. If they were suddenly hit by a storm at sea it was important that the sails were taken down with great speed and everything else on the decks was firmly battened down.

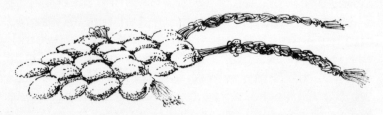

On the 13th April they came upon an island called Aitutaki. Three of the islanders came on board and surprised the sailors by falling on their knees and kissing William Bligh's feet. They gave the Captain a beautiful breastplate made of pearl shells and when he put it on, the crew noticed that the straps around his neck and over his shoulders were made of braided human hair.

In return the islanders were given knives and beads, two pigs, a boar and a sow. Bligh had intended that the people of Aitutaki should use the animals for breeding, but within hours the islanders were enjoying their first experience of roast pork - and enjoying it very much.

That night a whirlwind ripped past the ship as she lay at anchor. It was close enough to cause her to make an about - turn and face the way she had just come from. Perhaps this was an omen that soon the whole of the crew would be caught up in a different kind of storm.

A week later they reached the island of Nom-uka, the most easterly in the group that today we call the Islands of Tonga. In William Bligh's day they were known as the Friendly Isles but the welcome from the natives was the most un-friendly welcome the sailors had yet received.

The people were very different from the Tahitians. Women were not tattooed at all but had a design burnt onto their shoulders with hot bamboo sticks. The men were tattooed from their waist down to their knees which made them look as if they were wearing breeches. Everybody powdered their hair with lime or burnt seashells to make it appear either white, bright red or purple.

The islanders were friendly on the *Bounty* but on shore they prodded and teased the men. As Fletcher Christian led a party to collect fresh water from a spring, about a quarter of a mile inland, the islanders tried to take the water casks from the men just as they had tried to grab axes from them earlier in the day when they had been chopping wood. When Christian reported to William Bligh that the men were frightened and exasperated, Bligh called him a coward for being frightened of "a few naked savages while he had firearms." Fletcher Christian angrily replied that it was little use having guns when they were forbidden to use them.

Over the next few days the tension increased between the Captain and his second-in-command. On the 27th April a pile of coconuts stacked on the deck between the guns, vanished overnight and William Bligh accused Fletcher Christian of being a thief and a scoundrel who had joined the men to rob him.

The atmosphere on the *Bounty* had never been more difficult. Everybody felt involved in the dispute between the Captain and his second-in-command. It seemed to make Bligh angry with the whole crew.

Fletcher Christian was in a particularly delicate position. As master's mate he was really only a midshipman with the acting rank of Lieutenant and second-in-command. Not being an officer meant that the Captain could have him flogged if he did not behave and if this happened, Christian would lose the chance of promotion at the end of the voyage. So if he stood up to Bligh he would be punished, but if he did not, Bligh would make his life a misery.

Late on the 28th April 1789, Christian threw his personal papers overboard and gave away the mementos that he had collected in Tahiti for his family. He hid some left-over pork and Bread-fruit, and collected enough wood and rope to make a raft. It appears that Fletcher Christian intended at this point to escape from Bligh by slipping over the side of the ship at night when they passed close to an island.

45

At first light the next day he came on duty in charge of the watch. Up to this moment, the idea of mutiny does not seem to have occured to him. But as he woke a few of his friends, and, with them stole the key to the firearms from the armourer Joseph Coleman, mutiny obviously became his intention.

Arming themselves with cutlasses, pistols, muskets and bayonets they descended the ladderway to Bligh's cabin.

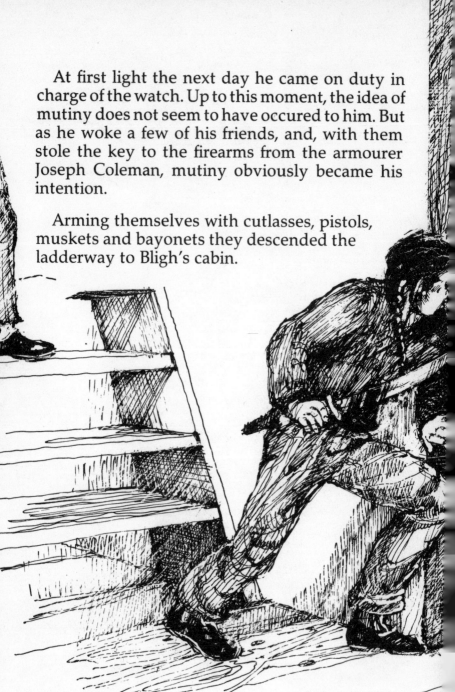

Flourishing cutlasses, Burkett, Mills and Churchill followed Fletcher Christian as he rushed in to wake up the Captain crying "Bligh you are my prisoner!"

After tying William Bligh's hands behind his back the mutineers dragged him up on deck forcing him to stand just in front of the ship's wheel.

Fletcher Christian held an end of the rope that secured him in one hand and with the other hand, he pressed a bayonet into Bligh's chest. Losing no more time, he ordered that the small cutter should be put to sea and that Thomas Hayward and John Hallet should be among its occupants. However, it soon become obvious that the small cutter had a leak and was not seaworthy.

Even the large cutter was not big enough for all those who wanted to go with William Bligh and they had to plead with Fletcher Christian to let them take the ship's launch. Reluctantly he agreed and then announced, "Come Captain Bligh. Your officers and men are now in the boat and you must go with them. If you attempt to make the least resistance you will be put to death." Without any further ado a group of mutineers untied his hands and Bligh was pushed over the *Bounty's* side.

Once their Captain was in the boat the pleading and the jeering ceased but frantic bargaining for more equipment continued. Christian consented to giving Bligh his own compass and grudgingly agreed that they might have four cutlasses in case they needed to defend themselves and further food and clothing was thrown down to them. They were then finally cut adrift.

The island of Tofua was close at hand and was the obvious place for Captain Bligh and his companions to head for. They knew it would not be too difficult to find because an active volcano marked its position clearly both by day and by night.

However, they soon discovered that the natives were far from friendly. John Norton the Quartermaster was killed in a stone-throwing battle and the others only managed to escape the same fate by leaving clothing and equipment on the beach. Out of curiosity, the natives were distracted by the things that had been abandoned and as they examined every article, the sailors in the open boat had time to escape.

51

Once clear of the island, Bligh announced that they were going to head for Timor which was over three thousand nautical miles away.

They checked their supplies and found that they had 150lbs of ship's biscuit, 28 gallons of water, 20lbs of salted pork, 10 pints of rum, 3 bottles of wine, some coconuts and Bread-fruit. The men agreed to ration themselves meagrely to 1 ounce of biscuit and a ¼ pint of water each day.

It is difficult to imagine the misery of that journey.

It was a tiny boat, only measuring 23 feet stem to stern so there was no room to lie down, not even one at a time. They had no charts or maps. It rained for twenty-one of the forty-three days that they were at sea.

Like a good Captain, William Bligh noted every-thing in his log. It was only because of his ability as a navigator that the journey was possible at all.

The food in the boat had to last a long time and fierce quarrels could easily start if someone appeared to have more food than anyone else. To make sure rations were fair, they were measured by a set of scales made out of coconut shells. A musket bullet was the weight used to balance each sailor's daily ration of ship's biscuit. Weakened by hunger and suffering terrible stomach pains, everyone had to face the possibility of death.

On the 25th May, after nearly a month at sea, the ration had to be reduced still further. But four days later the bedraggled crew passed through the Great Barrier Reef and landed in Australia. The safety of land changed the mood of the sailors, but because they were so weak and unwell they were still quarrelsome. They argued about how to make oyster stew and someone stole the remaining few pounds of salted pork.

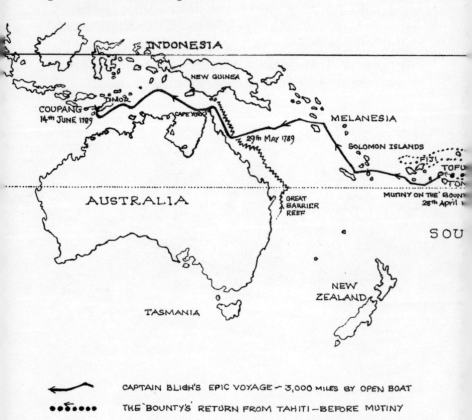

INDONESIA

NEW GUINEA

COUPANG
14th JUNE 1789

TIMOR

CAPE YORK

29th MAY 1789

MELANESIA

SOLOMON ISLANDS

FIJI

TOFU

TON

MUTINY ON THE BOUNTY
28th April

AUSTRALIA

GREAT
BARRIER
REEF

SOU

NEW
ZEALAND

TASMANIA

CAPTAIN BLIGH'S EPIC VOYAGE ~ 3,000 MILES BY OPEN BOAT

THE 'BOUNTY'S' RETURN FROM TAHITI ~ BEFORE MUTINY

THE COURSE OF THE 'BOUNTY' SAILED BY FLETCHER
CHRISTIAN AND THE MUTINEERS ~ AFTER A JOURNEY OF 8,000 miles
THEY FINALLY FOUND PITCAIRN ~ THE SAFE HAVEN ~ ON THE EVENING
OF 15th JANUARY 1790.

Once back at sea they again headed for Timor. During the voyage William Bligh became seriously ill. On the 12th June 1789 they sighted Timor. Filthy and exhausted, they had to be towed into Coupang as day broke on the 14th June.

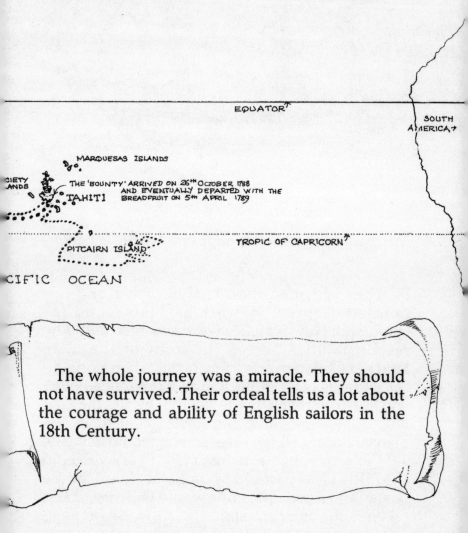

EQUATOR

SOUTH AMERICA→

MARQUESAS ISLANDS

CIETY
ANDS

THE 'BOUNTY' ARRIVED ON 26th OCTOBER 1788
AND EVENTUALLY DEPARTED WITH THE
TAHITI   BREADFRUIT ON 5th APRIL 1789

PITCAIRN ISLAND   TROPIC OF CAPRICORN

CIFIC   OCEAN

The whole journey was a miracle. They should not have survived. Their ordeal tells us a lot about the courage and ability of English sailors in the 18th Century.

We must now see what happened to the *Bounty*.

Fletcher Christian took charge of her and appointed George Stewart as his second-in-command. New watches were arranged and new responsibilities agreed. In front of the men, Fletcher Christian acted firmly but when alone, he sat with his head in his hands, probably anxious and also frightened by the fact that he and the men with him were now mutineers. They had disobeyed orders, stolen the ship and would never be able to return home as free men. Every vessel in the British Navy would be on the look-out for the *Bounty* and if seen, her crew would be arrested and taken home as prisoners.

The nine men aboard the *Bounty* were good sailors but they looked a dishevelled lot in their working clothes. They decided to make uniforms so they could all feel part of a team and also impress the natives of any island they decided to visit.

So it was that on the 30th April, two days after the mutiny, Fletcher Christian ordered the royals, which were small sails high on the mast, to be cut up as uniforms. On the 2nd May they cut up the mizzen and main staysails to create more jackets.

Early in May the crew threw the Bread-fruit saplings overboard and so were free to sail wherever they wished. But every day they must have lived with the fear of being caught.

To demonstrate his new position as leader of the mutineers Fletcher Christian moved into Bligh's small book-lined cabin. He then ordered that they set course for Tubuai, 350 nautical miles south of Tahiti.

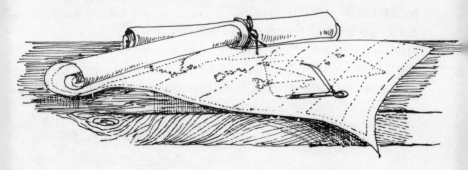

At first sight, Tubuai looked like two islands, one flat with a hill at the centre and the other high and rocky without any flat land at all. In fact it was one island. Instead of Tahiti's black volcanic sand there were dazzling white beaches. Like most Pacific islands, heavily scented flowers grew in profusion as did Bread-fruit, coconuts, yams and bananas. There were no animals, apart from rats, but plenty of fish, eel and wild duck. The islanders built little oval houses with thatched sides and roofs so that they looked like small haystacks. In spite of the fact that the people were much more violent than the Tahitians, this seemed to be the place where Fletcher Christian wanted to settle.

Bounty sailed through the one opening in the reef into Bloody Bay and almost immediately Fletcher Christian went ashore and established a settlement called Fort George. The Union Jack was hoisted on a makeshift flag-pole. They dug an 18 foot wide moat ready for walls which were to be 20 feet high, 18 feet wide at the base and 12 feet wide at the top. They made a quick journey back to Tahiti to collect some of the women they had become friendly with while there with Captain Bligh. They hoped to find the carefree life that they wanted. However, they were disappointed because the Tubuaians continued to be warlike and on the 14th July there was a terrible battle when 60 of the islanders were killed. This convinced Fletcher Christian that the island of Tubuai definitely was not the paradise that he was looking for.

The *Bounty* sailed back to Tahiti but could not stay long because of the risk of discovery. Tahiti was the one place in the Pacific that any ship from Europe would head for in search of the mutineers. So they would have to put to sea again but that was a problem because the *Bounty* was difficult to sail with a crew of only nine.

Tahitian men would only join the ship's crew if their women came too. But the women were not easily persuaded to come on board and so in the end had to be kidnapped.

Early on the morning of the 23rd September 1789, Fletcher Christian cut the cable, leaving the *Bounty*'s anchor behind, and slipped through the reef. On board were his eight companions, six Tahitian men, nineteen women and a little girl, 35 people in all.

They zigzagged about the Pacific Ocean looking for an uninhabited island where they could hide and one that was off the beaten track, so difficult for a searching ship to approach. By now the *Bounty* had ceased to look like one of His Majesty's ships. The months in the tropics had warped the deck timbers and most of the sails had been cut up or given away. They only had one small service-able boat to use.

At last, on the 15th January 1790, after four months of sailing 8,000 nautical miles about the Pacific Ocean, they spotted Pitcairn Island. Pitcairn was a lonely uninhabited rock less than two miles square. The sort of day that was calm enough to approach Pitcairn's rocky coast only happened once or twice in a man's lifetime but they only had to wait for two days before they could land.

The first few days on Pitcairn were very hard work. Everything that could be used was taken from the *Bounty* and carried ashore and up the steep cliffs. As it was an uninhabited island, there were no paths so a way had to be cut through the dense forest of trees and undergrowth.

After the months at sea, having left Tahiti on the 23rd September, everybody enjoyed being able to eat fresh fruit and vegetables again. The rocks were encrusted with every kind of shellfish, the sea was full of fish and teemed with delicious crayfish. Above the sea-level the rocky ledges were covered with nesting sea-birds which provided an abundance of fresh eggs. As soon as the animals were taken ashore they quickly became fat on the lush vegetation and started to breed. Fresh meat would never again be in short supply.

The *Bounty* had been run aground on the rocks directly below a 700 foot high cliff that they called *Ship Landing Point*. They named the bay *Bounty Bay*.

The seasons are reversed in the southern part of the world so January was the height of Pitcairn's summer with the temperature in the middle 90's, not the best weather for moving all the ship's equipment onto the land.

They made their first homes on the cliff among the trees so that they could not be spotted from the sea. These were shelters which were made by using some of the ship's timbers as roofing frames and then covering them with what was left of the sails and a ready supply of giant palm leaves.

Fletcher Christian had now discovered the paradise that he was looking for.

While the *Bounty* was being unloaded, Fletcher Christian realised that the ship might easily be spotted by a passing vessel. After all, the mast and spars of a square-rigger are not easy to hide and would stand out against the sky and silhouette of the island.

So, on the 23rd January after everything that was movable had been taken ashore, the *Bounty* was set alight. The sun-dried timbers, caulked and waterproofed with tar, burnt quickly. The fire devoured the wood of the ship and then the copper sheathing of the hull slipped below the waves to the sea-bed.

Pitcairn Island was to be divided equally between Fletcher Christian and the other eight mutineers. Some of the Tahitians with them were chiefs but they were not given land and became the servants and labourers to be used by the men from the *Bounty* as they wished. Sadly the democracy that at this time was gaining such favour in France and America, was not going to be tolerated on Pitcairn. A new social order came into being which put Fletcher Christian in sole authority and charge. He was the island's leader, and under him the other landowners and Tahitians were made to serve.

Life quickly settled down to some sort of normality. Permanent homes had to be built and the land cultivated.

The first baby was born later that first year to Fletcher Christian's Tahitian wife, Isabella. There could not possibly be any doubt about the baby's birthday because he was christened, Friday October Christian. Eventually he had a brother called Charles and a little sister as well.

Plenty of food, no work and a lot of sunshine sounds like the sort of life most people dream about. But for the people on Pitcairn Island it quickly became a nightmare. Fletcher Christian and his companions chose the Tahitian women they wanted as their wives and the Tahitian men had to share those that were left. This and the way the Tahitians were expected to be servants and slaves of the mutineers meant that arguments and fighting were inevitable. Two years after landing on Pitcairn, the Tahitian men went on the rampage and killed at least four of the men from the *Bounty*, John Williams, John Mills, Isaac Marting and William Brown. Fletcher Christian was probably killed on this occasion as well. There is just the possibility that he might have survived the shooting, hiding afterwards to recover from his wounds in a cave that is known today as Christian's Cave.

Alcohol created another problem for the people on the island. At home William McKoy had once worked in a Scottish whisky distillery and he discovered a way of extracting alcohol from the roots of the Ti-Tree trees, using the *Bounty*'s copper kettle as a still.

The men had little else to do except drink and once in a drunken state fierce bickering and fighting broke out.

It is strange that nobody is certain about how or where Fletcher Christian died. Some people say that he built a boat and managed to escape from Pitcairn eventually making his way back to England. This has become a legend that links him with Samuel Taylor Coleridge's famous poem 'The Rime of the Ancient Mariner', but there is no real evidence for this.

Samuel Taylor Coleridge was a friend of Christian's parents so it is just possible that Coleridge had some inside information about the fate of Fletcher Christian. He did at one time intend to write a book called 'The Adventure of Fletcher Christian.' The notebooks he used to begin making notes for this can still be seen.

In 1796 a newspaper called *The Weekly Entertainer* published an article that was supposed to be written by Christian giving his side of the story of the mutiny. However, William Wordsworth, another poet from the Lake District near Fletcher Christian's birthplace, wrote to the newspaper saying he had evidence that the article was false.

Could Wordsworth and Coleridge have been in touch with Fletcher Christian? We do not really know the answer to that. Towards the end of his life John Adams, one of the longest surviving men from the original group on Pitcairn hinted that Fletcher Christian had escaped from the island in a boat. Peter Heywood, a former midshipman on the *Bounty* and a man who knew Fletcher Christian, was certain that he saw him in Devonport. So Christian could have returned to England, told his story to Coleridge who instead of writing about it in a book, put it all into the poem which we now know as 'The Rime of the Ancient Mariner'.

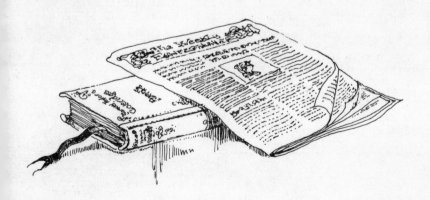

It would be wrong to think that the fighting on Pitcairn was simply between the mutineers and the Tahitians. The truth was that everybody fought everybody else. Of the fifteen men who landed on Pitcairn, four years later, eleven had been murdered. Some of the sailors remained in such a continuous state of drunkenness that they went out of their minds or committed suicide.

The men were obviously more savage than the women, but the women were not above committing or arranging the murder of a man who had hurt them or upset them. What should have been an earthly paradise of fun, food, relaxation and family relationships, became a depraved state where people behaved little better than animals. Indeed, animals would not have been so brutal.

The fighting ceased to some extent when the women took the children and barricaded themselves into a part of the island which could only be approached by a narrow path. The way to the women's camp was impassable unless the women chose themselves to remove the barrier. They swore that they would never again have anything to do with the men. They seemed happy to live without any contact with them if it meant that they could live in quietness and peace with their children.

By the time the women chose to live separately, nine years had passed since their arrival on the island. Now only two men remained, with the eleven women and twenty children barricaded away at one end of Pitcairn.

The two remaining men were John Adams who had previously used the name Alexander Smith, and Edward Young. Adams was from the East End of London and had been brought up in a poor house so could not read. Edward Young was reasonably well educated. As they began to reminisce about the past and the old days in England, nostalgia set them looking for anything that would remind them of England. In their search they rediscovered the ship's box which contained the *Bounty*'s Bible and Prayer Book.

Edward Young started to teach John Adams to read by using the Bible. He opened it at Genesis and began to read making John Adams follow with his finger word for word along the page. By the time they reached the Psalms they realised they were songs and tried to sing them, even though they did not know any tunes.

Before they finished reading the Old Testament Edward Young who suffered from asthma, died, but now John Adams could read well enough to continue.

Once he had begun the New Testament he had a deep and profound christian experience that completely changed his life. It undoubtedly saved the community on Pitcairn from being completely destroyed.

The women had begun to realise that a change was taking place in the lives of the two men. Once they had found the ship's Bible and prayer book and started to read them, they no longer seemed to spend their time drinking as wildly as before and they weren't fighting and quarrelling so much now.

The women and children felt it was now safe to creep out from behind their barricades. At first they were suspicous of the change in the men, thinking that it might be only temporary. But gradually they saw this it was permanent and lasting.

The barricades came down and John Adams became the island's teacher for the children and Pastor to the adults. The old days of drunkenness and fighting were gone for ever.

Life on the island returned to some form of normality. Farming and fishing were daytime duties and these were interspersed with times of fun when everybody flew kites, walked on stilts or practised 'sliding', the Pitcairner's form of surfing They used a broad tray that resembled 'a butcher's tray' which was rounded at one end and square at the other. A later report which is nearly two hundred years old, describes it like this,

> "Islanders amuse themselves by taking a flat board, about three feet long, on the upper side smooth and on the under a ridge like a keel, and went out on a rock and waited till a large wave came and when the top of it was close to them, away they went with the piece of wood under their stomachs on top of the wave and directing themselves by their feet into the little channels formed by the rocks."

It must have been very exciting.

When Captain Cook first visited Tahiti he said that there was no surfing and he concluded that it must be unique to the Sandwich Islands; today we call them the Hawaiian Islands.

In 1808 Pitcairn Island had its first visitors since
the arrival of the mutineers. They were on the
Topaz, a whaling ship that had sailed from Boston
on the East Coast of America. Sailing across the
Northern part of the Pacific Ocean the *Topaz* came
across Pitcairn Island and as it was not marked on
any of their charts, the Captain presumed it was
uninhabited.

In his log, Captain Folger tells what happened;
"I discovered a boat paddling towards me." It was
a Tahitian style canoe containing three young
men "as dark as natives" and almost naked. The
natives surprised the crew by yelling to them in
English! The seamen called back that they were
from America.

"America? Is that in Ireland?"
"No - A long way from there. What is your race?"
"We are English"
"How can that be?"
"Because our father was English"
"Who was your father?"
"Aleck"
"Who is Aleck?"
"Don't you know Aleck?"
"How should we?"
"Well then, do you know Captain Bligh?"

The light began to dawn on the Captain and the crew of the *Topaz* as they realised they had found the descendants of the mutineers from the *Bounty*.

Once John Adams realised that he was not going to be arrested, he relaxed and asked for news of the rest of the world.

Captain Folger told him about the French Revolution, Napoleon's rise to power and explained that England and France were now at war. He then recounted Nelson's great victory at Trafalgar which an old sailor like John Adams found very moving. He stood up "took off his hat, swinging it three times round his head with three cheers" and then threw it on the ground shouting "Old England forever!"

In checking the island's exact position on the map it was discovered that the Pitcairners were one day out in their calendar. Captain Folger suggested the reason for this might be that the mutineers had forgotten to alter the date when they crossed the date-line on their voyage to Pitcairn in 1789. It did not really matter to anyone except Friday October Christian who had to change his name to Thursday October Christian.

Captain Mayhew Folger's report speaks of a people who were "tall, robust and golden-limbed." He says that not only was everyone on the island very athletic and good at surfing, but also that nobody stole, lied or drank. He added that they all appeared to live to help other people.

A copy of this report by Captain Folger was sent to the Admiralty in 1809 and was followed up with a personal letter in 1813. We know the difference the reading of the ship's Bible made to the islanders of Pitcairn because we can still read Captain Folger's report and letter today. It was published in the *Quarterly Review* in February 1810.

Glyn Christian, the TV cook and great, great great grandson of the original mutineer has said recently about the discovery of the island, "Something awesome and biblical happened between 1790 and 1808. Pitcairn was not the expected group of middle-aged men and women with their children. Instead, the island was like Eden."

It must be one of those strange quirks of history that a community which was started by a handful of violent mutineers and who openly practised terror and bloodshed on each other in the early years of their life on the island, had now become a model society of peace and order.

The transformation can be traced back directly to the discovery of the ship's Bible and Prayer Book and the change of life that John Adams experienced as a result of reading them. The life of the whole community was now directed and ordered by the Bible. They tried to follow its instructions and to live in God's way. In spite of the fact that John Adams was only in his early forties he now became the island's ancient patriarch, leader and pastor teacher.

In the coming days many ships called at Pitcairn now that its exact position was known in the Pacific Ocean. Each Captain, when making his report, would marvel at the way the Pitcairners managed to reflect the teaching of the Bible.

Captain Pipon of the *Targus* writes about Thursday October Christian visiting the ship just off the island, "he was a tall, fine young man about six feet high, with dark, black hair, and a face that was extremely open and interesting. He wore no clothes except a piece of cloth around his waist, and a straw hat ornamented with a black cock's feather, and an occasional peacock's feather similar to that worn by the Spaniards in South America".

It did not really matter what the people wore as long as their behaviour was right and it was the Pitcairners' godly way of life that was noticed by visiting travellers. Big communities like the country in which we live still have to discover this.

Pitcairn

DE
WA

HEADACHE

LITTLE GEORGE COC

BIG
SALLY

POINT CHRISTIAN

OH DEAR

GUDGEO

SOUTH
PACIFIC
OCEAN

STATUTE MILES

Island

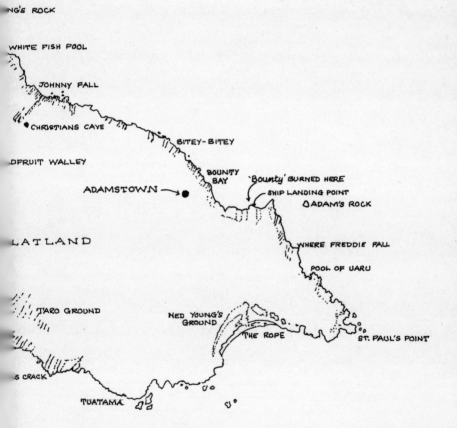

NG'S ROCK

WHITE FISH POOL

JOHNNY FALL

CHRISTIANS CAVE

BITEY-BITEY

DFRUIT WALLEY

BOUNTY BAY

ADAMSTOWN →

'Bounty' BURNED HERE

SHIP LANDING POINT

ADAM'S ROCK

LATLAND

WHERE FREDDIE FALL

POOL OF UARU

TARO GROUND

NED YOUNG'S GROUND

THE ROPE

ST. PAUL'S POINT

S CRACK

TUATAMA